Orchestra	602
Boxes	8
Front Mezzanine	264
Rear Mezzanine	251
Total	1,125

Mezzanine row A overhangs
Orchestra row H.

Wheelchair locations
K 28-30. 27-29
L 28-30, 27-29

FOR REFERENCE

*AMBASSADOR THEATRE

215 West 49th Street
New York, New York 10019

Box Office: (212) 239-6200
Group Sales: (212) 398-8383

STAGE

BOXES

C/D

BOXES

B/A

ORCHESTRA

FRONT MEZZANINE

REAR MEZZANINE

5

*BROOKS ATKINSON THEATRE

256 West 47th Street
New York, New York 10036

Box Office: (212) 307-4100
Group Sales: (212) 398-8383

Orchestra	612
Boxes	24
Mezzanine	156
Balcony	290
Total	1,082

Mezzanine row A overhangs
Orchestra row K.

Wheelchair locations
M 23-25, Q 21-23

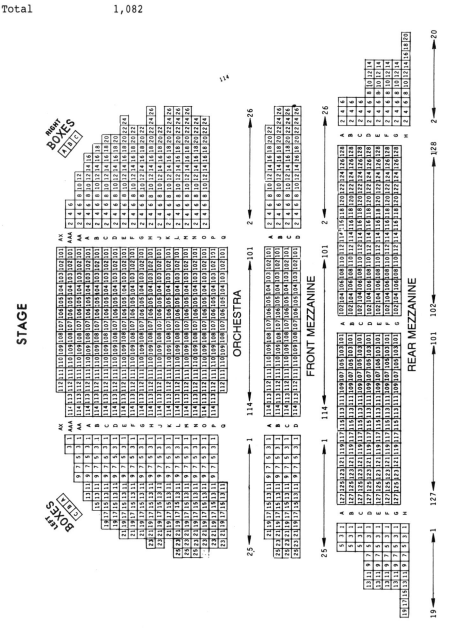

STAGE

ORCHESTRA

FRONT MEZZANINE

REAR MEZZANINE

RIGHT BOXES A B C

LEFT BOXES C B A

INDEX OF SEATING PLANS FOR METROPOLITAN NEW YORK

INDEX OF SEATING PLANS FOR METROPOLITAN NEW YORK

* ASTERISK DENOTES THAT A THEATRE IS EQUIPPED WITH AN INFRARED LISTENING SYSTEM.

WHEELCHAIR LOCATIONS HAVE BEEN INCLUDED AS PROVIDED BY EACH THEATRE. THE LISTINGS ARE NOT NECESSARILY COMPLETE.

Developing American playwrights Since 1949.

Seven years of free resources
for new writers. An artistic home.

write for membership information.

New Dramatists

424 West 44ᵗʰ Street, New York, NY 10036
(212) 757-6960 Fax: (212) 265-4738
For New Dramatists news on the World Wide Web
http://www.itp.tsoa.nyu.edu/~diana/ndintro.html

Judy Feder, Barry Carl and Stephen Kalm.   Photo by Christie Mullen.

* ETHEL BARRYMORE THEATRE

243 West 47th Street
New York, New York 10036

Box Office: (212) 239-6200
Group Sales: (212) 398-8383

Orchestra	620
Boxes	24
Front Mezzanine	196
Rear Mezzanine	256
Total	1,096

Front Mezzanine row A overhangs
Orchestra row K.

Wheelchair locations
M 23-25, Q 21-23

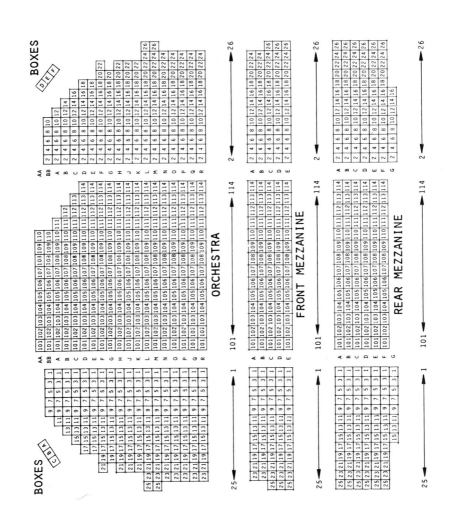

*BEACON THEATRE

2130 Broadway (at 74th Street)
New York, New York   10023

Box Office: (212) 496-7070

Ticket Purchases by Telephone Only.

Orchestra	1,384
Loge	542
Lower Balcony	281
Upper Balcony	501
Total	2,708

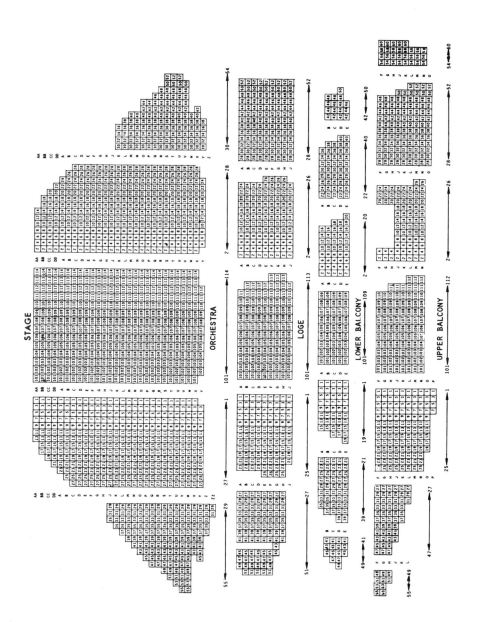

*VIVIAN BEAUMONT THEATER

Lincoln Center
150 West 65th Street
New York, New York 10023

Box Office: (212) 239-6200
Group Sales: (212) 398-8383

Orchestra	740
Loge	361
Total	1,101

Wheelchair
locations
O 111-112,
O 201-202,
O 401-402,
O 511-512

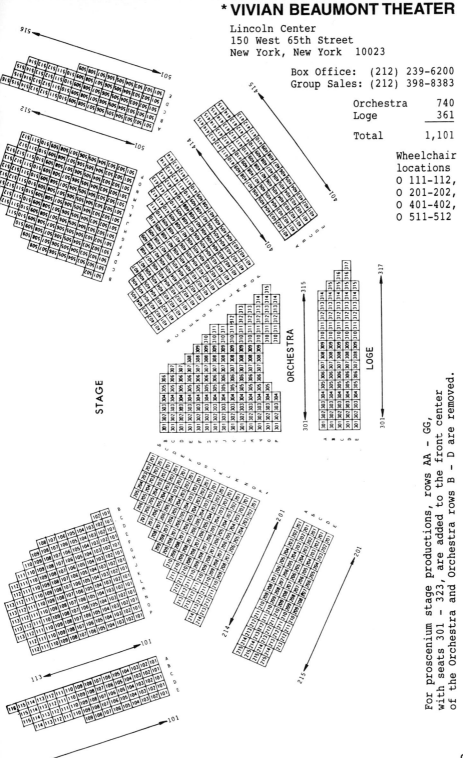

For proscenium stage productions, rows AA - GG,
with seats 301 - 323, are added to the front center
of the Orchestra and Orchestra rows B - D are removed.

9

*MARTIN BECK THEATRE

302 West 45th Street
New York, New York 10036

Box Office: (212) 239-6200
Group Sales: (212) 398-8383

Orchestra   720
Boxes   28
Mezzanine   666

Total   1,414

Mezzanine row A overhangs
Orchestra row J.

Wheelchair locations
H 19-21, J 23-25, H 20-22, J 24-26

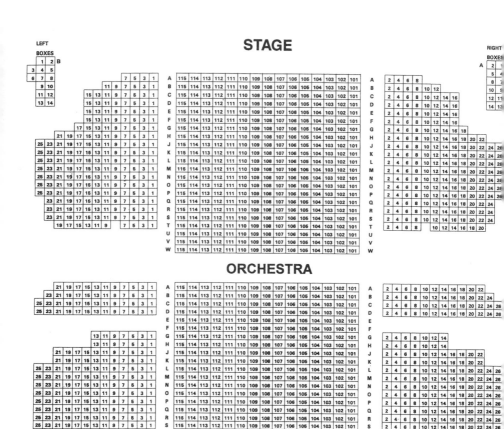

111 West 44th Street
New York, New York 10036

Mezzanine row A overhangs
Orchestra row J.
Balcony row A overhangs
Mezzanine row C.

Wheelchair locations N 23-25, O 26-28

Box Office: (212) 239-6200
Group Sales: (212) 398-8383

Orchestra	532
Mezzanine	285
Balcony	201
Total	1,018

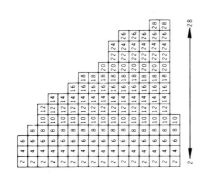
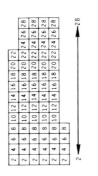
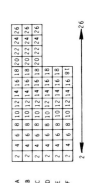

STAGE

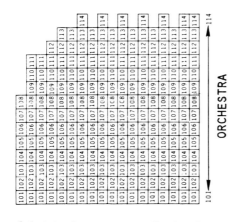

ORCHESTRA

MEZZANINE

BALCONY

*BOOTH THEATRE

222 West 45th Street
New York, New York 10036

Box Office: (212) 239-6200
Group Sales: (212) 398-8383

Orchestra	517
Boxes	12
Mezzanine	252
Total	781

Mezzanine row A overhangs
Orchestra row H.

Wheelchair locations Q 1-3, 2-4

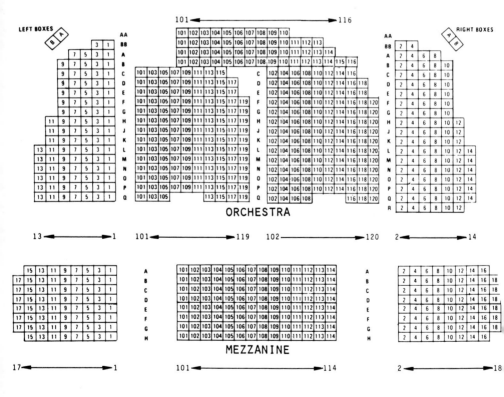

STAGE

ORCHESTRA

MEZZANINE

* BROADHURST THEATRE

235 West 44th Street
New York, New York 10036

Mezzanine row A overhangs
Orchestra row K.

Wheelchair locations
K 21-23, 22-24
L 25-27, 26,28

*Orchestra capacity for
musicals is 703 because
of the elimination of
rows AA and BB.

Box Office: (212) 239-6200
Group Sales: (212) 398-8383

Orchestra   733*
Boxes   24
Mezzanine   429

Total   1,186

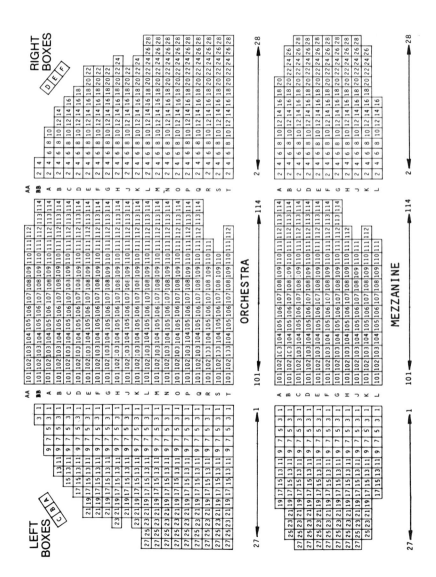

STAGE

13

*BROADWAY THEATRE

1681 Broadway (at 53rd Street)
New York, New York 10019

Box Office: (212) 239-6200
Group Sales: (212) 398-8383

Orchestra	906
Boxes	12
Front Mezzanine	250
Rear Mezzanine	584
Total	1,752

Front Mezzanine row A overhangs
Orchestra row J.

Wheelchair locations
F 16-18, 15-17, O 26-28, 25-27

STAGE

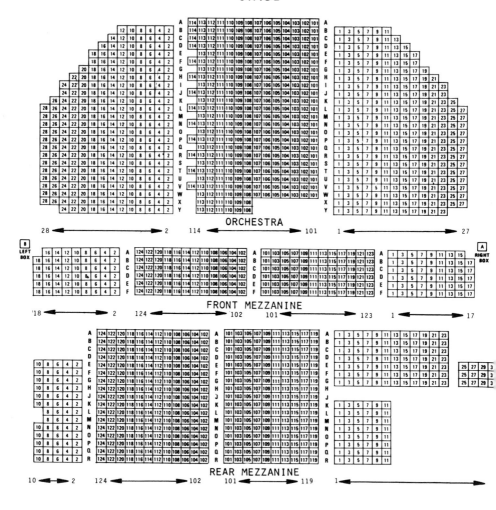

ORCHESTRA

FRONT MEZZANINE

REAR MEZZANINE

BRENDAN BYRNE ARENA

Meadowlands
East Rutherford, NJ 07073

Box Office: (201) 935-3900

Lower Tier	11,116
Upper Tier	9,982
Total	21,098

Wheelchair locations adjoining
boxes 102-105, 111-119, 125-128

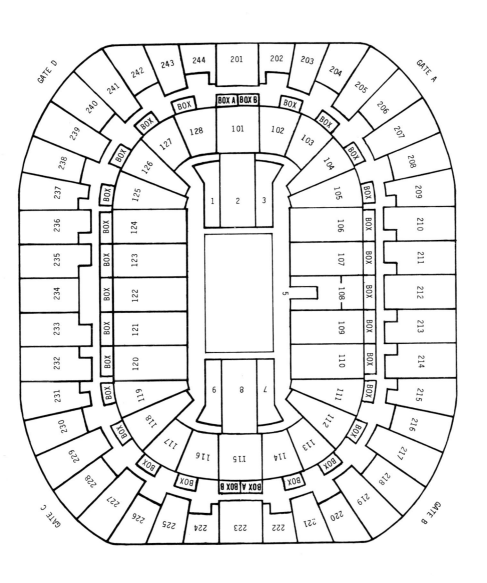

15

BROOKLYN ACADEMY OF MUSIC
MAJESTIC THEATER

651 Fulton Street
(at the corner of Rockwell Plaza)
Brooklyn, New York 11217

Box Office: (212) 307-4100
Group Sales: (212) 398-8383

Orchestra	252
Gallery	241
Total	893

Wheelchair locations M 21-25, 22-26

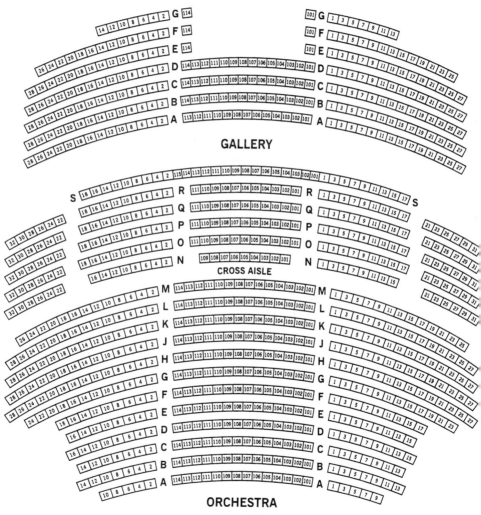

GALLERY

CROSS AISLE

ORCHESTRA

STAGE

BROOKLYN ACADEMY OF MUSIC
THE OPERA HOUSE

Mezzanine row A overhangs
Orchestra row L.
Balcony row A overhangs
Mezzanine row D.

Wheelchair locations
V 1, 2, 24, 26, 27, 38, 41

30 Lafayette Street
Brooklyn, New York 11217

Box Office: (212) 307-4100
Group Sales: (212) 398-8383

Orchestra	934
Boxes	48
Mezzanine	574
Balcony	530
Total	2,086

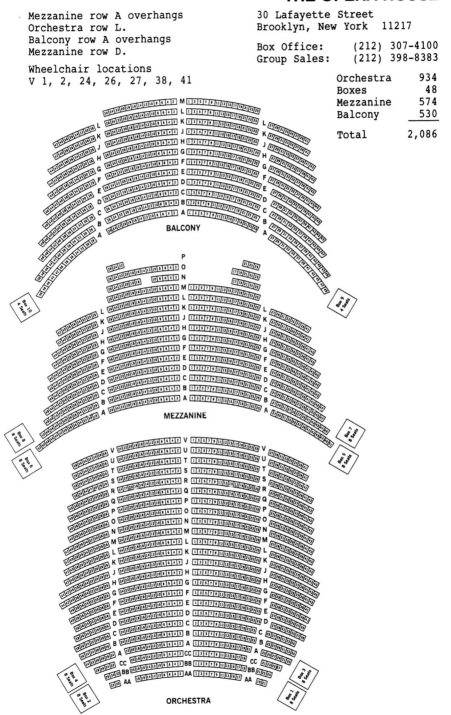

BALCONY

MEZZANINE

ORCHESTRA

STAGE

17

*CARNEGIE HALL

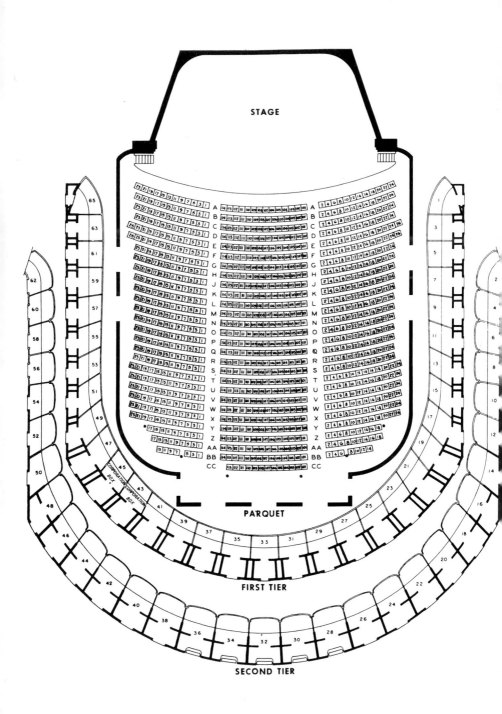

* CARNEGIE HALL

154 West 57th Street
New York, New York 10019

Box Office: (212) 247-7800

Parquet	1,021
First Tier Boxes	264
Second Tier Boxes	238
Dress Circle	444
Balcony	837
Total	2,804

Wheelchair locations
Parquet B and C
    1, 3, 21, 23
    2, 4, 22, 24

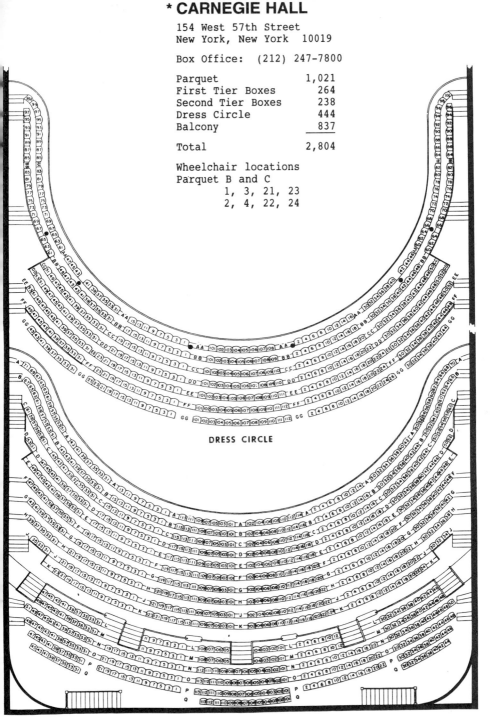

DRESS CIRCLE

BALCONY

*CITY CENTER

131 West 55th Street
New York, New York 10019

Box Office: (212) 581-1212
Group Sales: (212) 398-8383

Orchestra	699
Grand Tier	258
Front Mezzanine	394
Rear Mezzanine	568
Gallery	765
Total	2,684

Grand Tier row A overhangs
Orchestra row G.

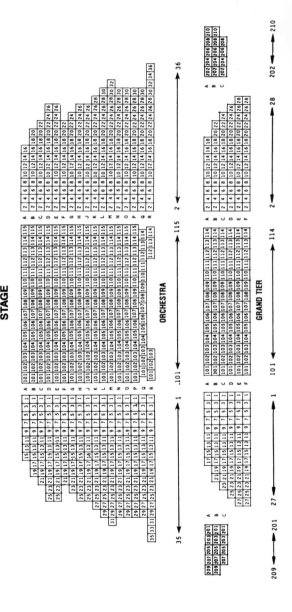

STAGE

ORCHESTRA

GRAND TIER

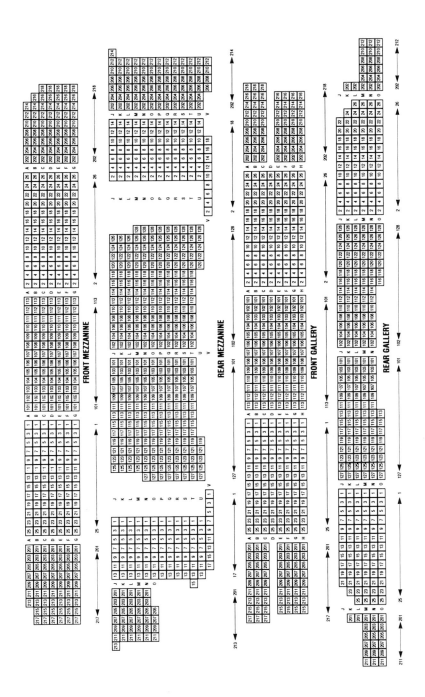

FRONT MEZZANINE

REAR MEZZANINE

FRONT GALLERY

REAR GALLERY

*CIRCLE IN THE SQUARE

1633 Broadway at 50th Street
New York, New York 10019

Box Office: (212) 239-6200
Group Sales: (212) 398-8383

Theatre Capacity: 681

Wheelchair locations
G 301-303, 302-304

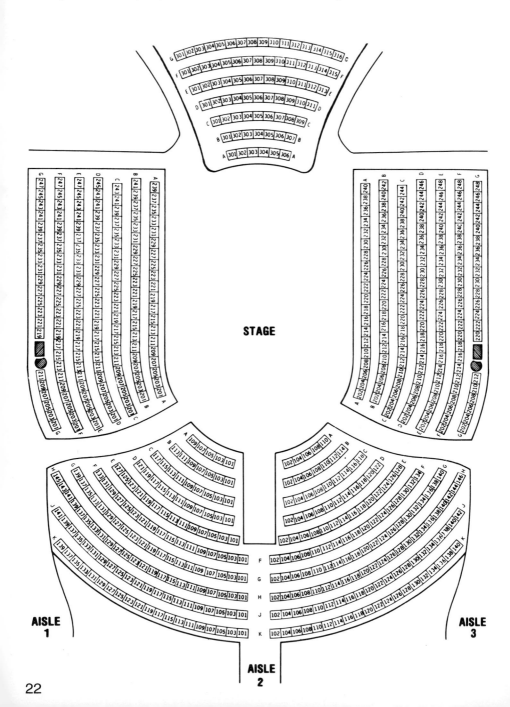

STAGE

AISLE 1

AISLE 2

AISLE 3

22

*CORT THEATRE

138 West 48th Street
New York, New York 10036

Mezzanine row A overhangs
Orchestra row J.

Wheelchair locations L 21-23, M 21-23

| Box Office: | (212) 239-6200 |
| Group Sales: | (212) 398-8383 |

Orchestra	505
Boxes	32
Mezzanine	264
Balcony	283
Total	1,084

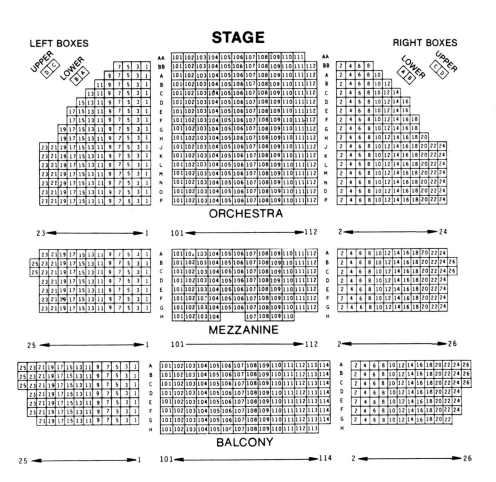

LEFT BOXES — STAGE — RIGHT BOXES

ORCHESTRA

MEZZANINE

BALCONY

23

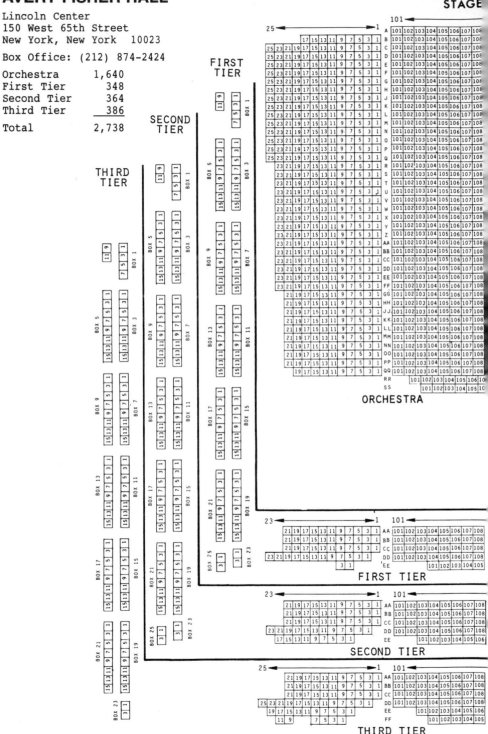

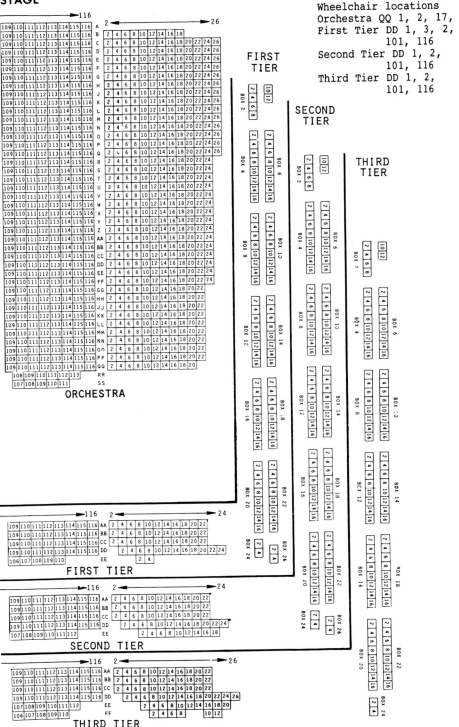

AVERY FISHER HALL

STAGE

FIRST TIER

SECOND TIER

THIRD TIER

ORCHESTRA

FIRST TIER

SECOND TIER

THIRD TIER

25

*FORD CENTER
FOR THE PERFORMING ARTS

213 West 42nd Street
New York, New York 10036

Box Office: (212) 307-4100
Group Sales: (212) 398-8383

Orchestra	1,096
Dress Circle	343
Dress Circle Boxes	26
Balcony	319
Balcony Boxes	24
Total	**1,808**

Dress Circle row A overhangs
Orchestra row T.
Balcony row A overhangs
Dress Circle row B.

Wheelchair locations G 1-11, 2-12

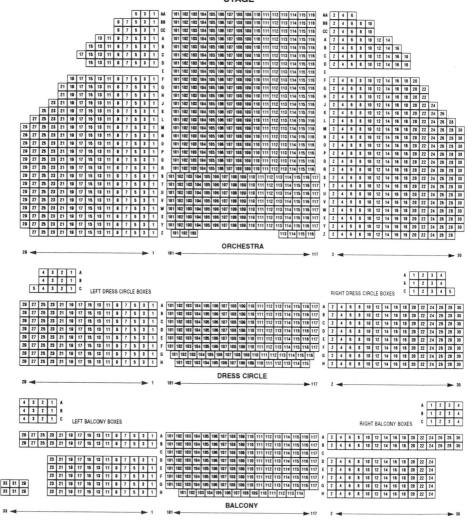

STAGE

ORCHESTRA

LEFT DRESS CIRCLE BOXES   RIGHT DRESS CIRCLE BOXES

DRESS CIRCLE

LEFT BALCONY BOXES   RIGHT BALCONY BOXES

BALCONY

Mezzanine row A overhangs
Orchestra row N.

Wheelchair locations
ZZ 11-13, 15-17, 16-18

| Box Office: | (212) 307-4100 |
| Group Sales: | (212) 398-8383 |

Orchestra	1,298
Loge	46
Front Mezzanine	247
Rear Mezzanine	342
Total	1,933

STAGE

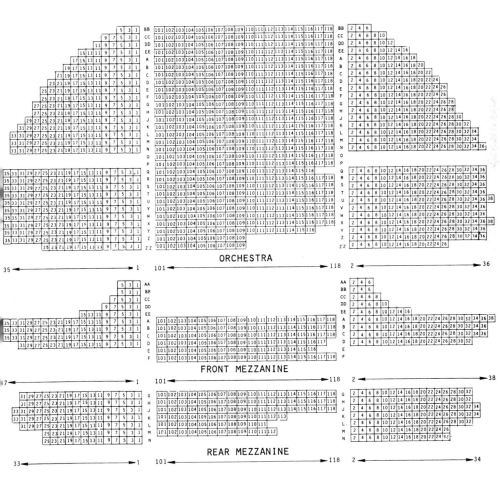

ORCHESTRA

FRONT MEZZANINE

REAR MEZZANINE

*JOHN GOLDEN THEATRE

252 West 45th Street
New York, New York 10036

Box Office: (212) 239-6200
Group Sales: (212) 398-8383

Orchestra	468
Front Mezzanine	110
Rear Mezzanine	227
Total	805

Front Mezzanine row A overhangs
Orchestra row L.

Wheelchair locations
E 121-123, E 124-126

STAGE

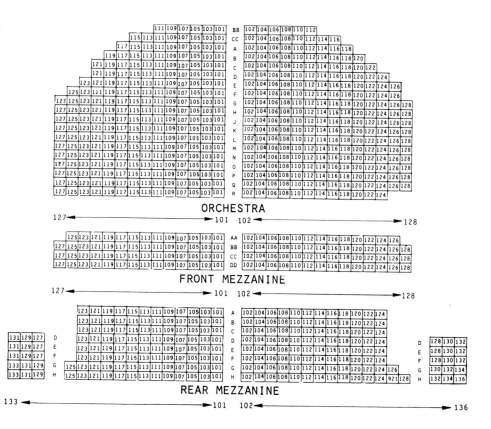

ORCHESTRA

FRONT MEZZANINE

REAR MEZZANINE

28

* HELEN HAYES THEATRE

240 West 44th Street
New York, New York 10036

Box Office: (212) 307-4100
Group Sales: (212) 398-8383

Orchestra	379
Mezzanine	218
Total	597

Mezzanine row A overhangs
Orchestra row J.

Wheelchair locations A 1-3, 2-4

STAGE

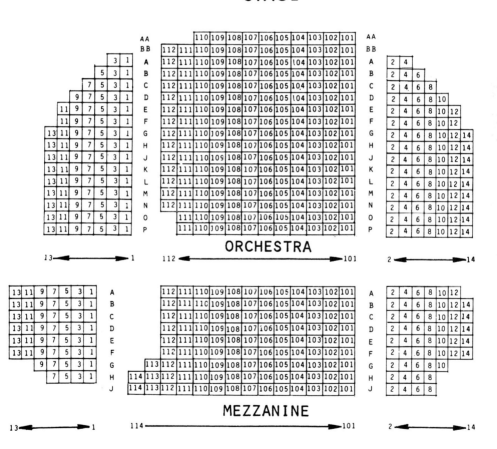

ORCHESTRA

MEZZANINE

*IMPERIAL THEATRE

249 West 45th Street
New York, New York 10036

Box Office: (212) 239-6200
Group Sales: (212) 398-8383

Mezzanine row A overhangs Orhcestra row H

Wheelchair locations K 25-27, L 25-27

Orchestra	737
Boxes	27
Front Mezzanine	283
Rear Mezzanine	374
Total	1,421

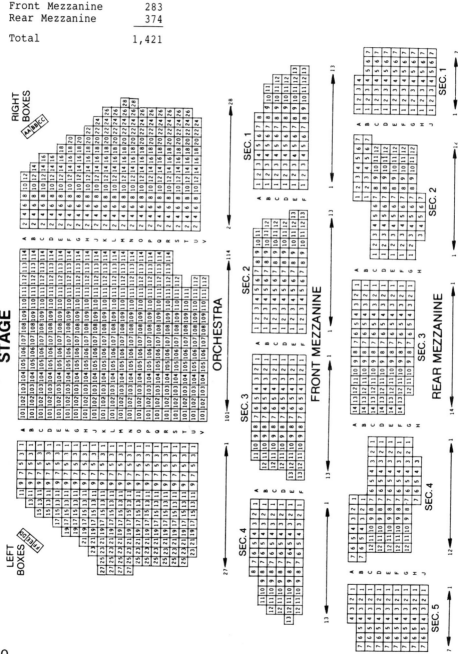

STAGE

RIGHT BOXES
AA BB CC

LEFT BOXES
DD EE FF

ORCHESTRA

FRONT MEZZANINE

REAR MEZZANINE

SEC. 1
SEC. 2
SEC. 3
SEC. 4
SEC. 5

THE JOYCE THEATRE

Theatre Capacity: 472

Wheelchair locations
A, B, D 2-10 & 1-9

175 Eighth Avenue (at 19th Street)
New York, New York 10011

Box Office: (212)242-0800

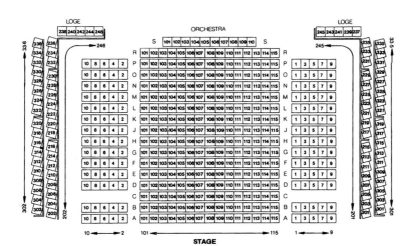

KAUFMANN CONCERT HALL

Orchestra   640
Balcony   276

Total   916

lcony row A overhangs Orchestra row S.
eelchair locations E 1-9, 2-10

92nd Street Y
Lexington Avenue at 92nd Street
New York, New York 10128

Y-Charge: (212) 996-1100
Box Office:(212) 415-5440

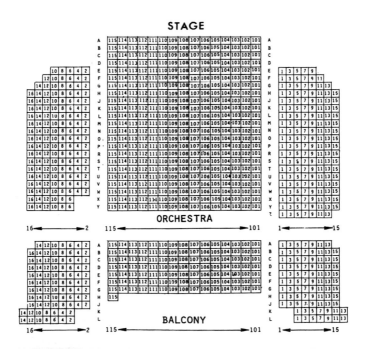

31

*THE SYLVIA & DANNY KAYE PLAYHOUSE

695 Park Avenue (at 68th Street)
New York, New York 10021

Box Office: (212) 772-4448

Orchestra   490
Balcony   170
Total   660

Mezzanine row A overhangs
Orchestra row L.

Wheelchair locations
all of row S, 16 locations

STAGE

ORCHESTRA

BALCONY

*WALTER KERR THEATRE

219 West 48th Street
New York, New York 10036

Mezzanine row A overhangs
Orchestra row J.

Wheelchair locations L 18-20, M 18-20
                     L 17-19, M 17-19

| Box Office: | (212) 239-6200 |
| Group Sales: | (212) 398-8383 |

Orchestra	543
Boxes	16
Mezzanine	322
Balcony	66
Total	947

STAGE

ORCHESTRA

MEZZANINE

BALCONY

33

KIT KAT KLUB AT HENRY MILLER'S THEATRE

124 West 43rd Street
New York, New York 10036

Box Office: (212) 239-6200
Group Sales: (212) 398-8383

Orchestra at Tables   208
Orchestra   52
Mezzanine at Tables   72
Mezzanine   132

Total   464

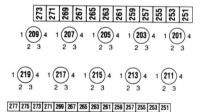

STAGE

ORCHESTRA

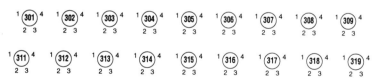

MEZZANINE

34

* LONGACRE THEATRE

220 West 48th Street
New York, New York 10036

Mezzanine row A overhangs Orchestra row K.
Balcony row A overhangs Mezzanine row B.

Wheelchair locations L 21-23, 22-24

Box Office: (212) 239-6200
Group Sales: (212) 398-8383

Orchestra	522
Boxes	16
Mezzanine	314
Balcony	243
Total	1,095

STAGE

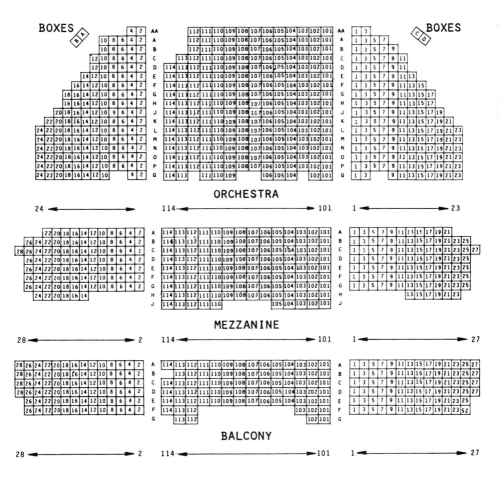

ORCHESTRA

MEZZANINE

BALCONY

*LUNT-FONTANNE THEATRE

205 West 46th Street
New York, New York 10036

Box Office: (212) 307-4100
Group Sales: (212) 398-8383

Orchestra   859
Boxes   20
Front Mezzanine   168
Rear Mezzanine   428

Total   1,475

Mezzanine row A overhangs
Orchestra row J.

Wheelchair locations X 11-13

STAGE

ORCHESTRA

BOX A   MEZZANINE LEFT   MEZZANINE RIGHT   BOX B

FRONT MEZZANINE

REAR MEZZANINE

*LYCEUM THEATRE

149 West 45th Street
New York, New York 10036

Box Office: (212) 239-6200
Group Sales: (212) 398-8383

Wheelchair locations L 15-17, 16-18

Mezzanine row A overhangs Orchestra row L.
Balcony row A overhangs Mezzanine row C.

Orchestra	411
Boxes	16
Mezzanine	287
Balcony	210
Total	924

Mezzanine row A overhangs
Orchestra row J.

Wheelchair locations
N 25-27, M 26-28

STAGE

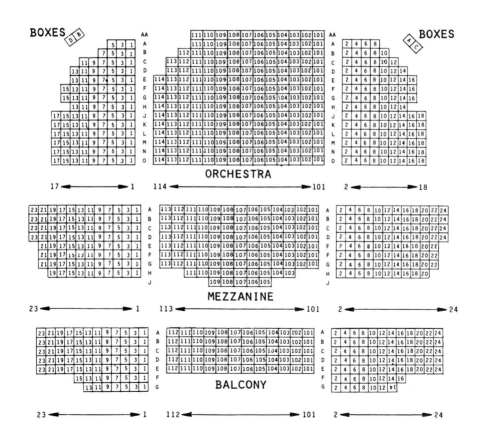

BOXES

BOXES

ORCHESTRA

17 ◄——► 1   114 ◄————► 101   2 ◄————► 18

MEZZANINE

23 ◄——► 1   113 ◄————► 101   2 ◄————► 24

BALCONY

23 ◄——► 1   112 ◄————► 101   2 ◄————► 24

37

*MADISON SQUARE GARDEN

4 Pennsylvania Plaza at 31st-33rd Streets
New York, New York 10001

Box Office: (212) 307-7171
Group Sales: (212) 398-8383

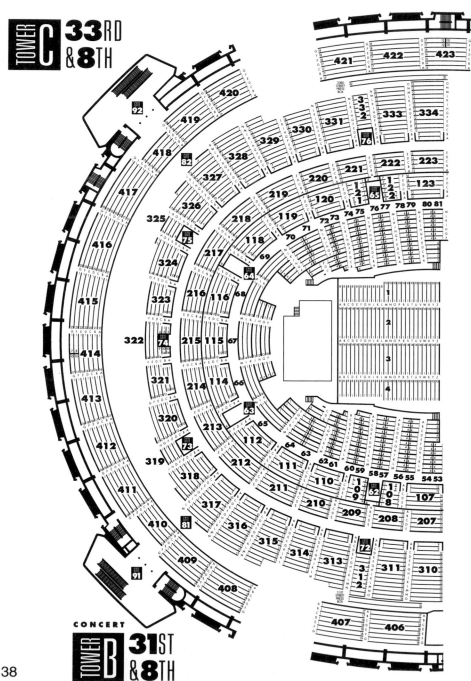

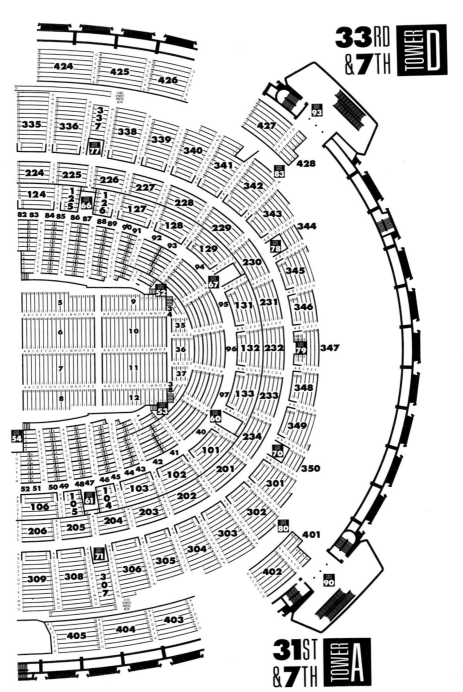

*MAJESTIC THEATRE

245 West 44th Street
New York, New York 10036

Box Office:	(212) 239-6200	
Group Sales:	(212) 398-8383	
Orchestra	859	
Boxes	20	
Front Mezzanine	292	
Rear Mezzanine	436	
Total	1,607	

Orchestra is elevated starting at row K.
Front Mezzanine row A overhangs
Orchestra row J.

Wheelchair locations B 17
C 16-18, 17-19
D 16-18, 17
H 21-23

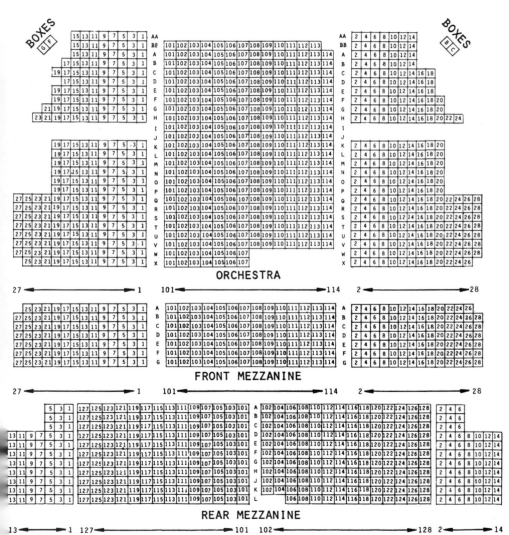

STAGE

ORCHESTRA

FRONT MEZZANINE

REAR MEZZANINE

Orchestra	1010
Mezzanine	585
Total	1,595

Mezzanine row A overhangs Orchestra row M.
Wheelchair locations Y 101-104, 116-119

*MARQUIS THEATRE

1535 Broadway (at 46th Street)
New York, New York 10036

Box Office: (212) 307-4100
Group Sales: (212) 398-8383

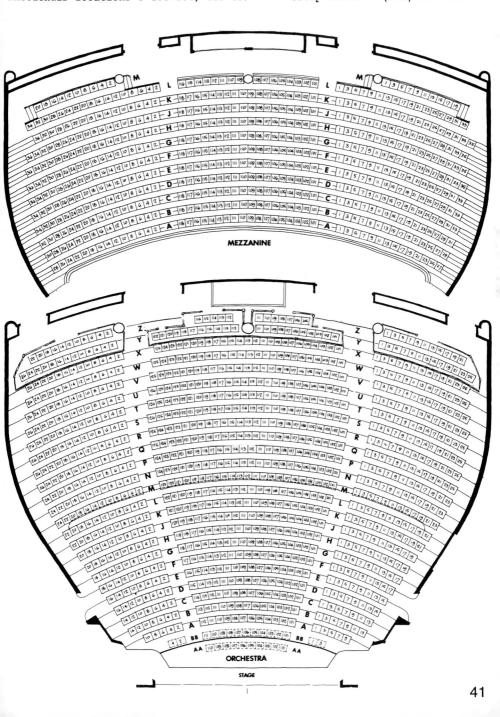

MEZZANINE

ORCHESTRA

STAGE

*METROPOLITAN OPERA HOUSE

Lincoln Center
Broadway at 64th Street
New York, New York 10023

Box Office: (212) 362-6000

Orchestra	1,583
Parterre Boxes	228
Grand Tier	454
Dress Circle	458
Balcony	362
Family Circle	633
Total	3,718

Wheelchair locations
Orchestre EE 1, 35, 2, 36
Dress Circle G 101, 129, 1, 25
            G 102, 130, 2, 26

STAGE

ORCHESTRA

FAMILY CIRCLE BOXES
BALCONY BOXES
DRESS CIRCLE BOXES
GRAND TIER BOXES
RIGHT   PARTERRE BOXES

LEFT   PARTERRE BOXES
GRAND TIER BOXES
DRESS CIRCLE BOXES
BALCONY BOXES
FAMILY CIRCLE BOXES

METROPOLITAN OPERA HOUSE

Parterre Boxes seat 8.
Grand Tier Boxes seat 6.
Dress Circle and Balcony Boxes seat 6.
Family Circle Boxes seat 3.

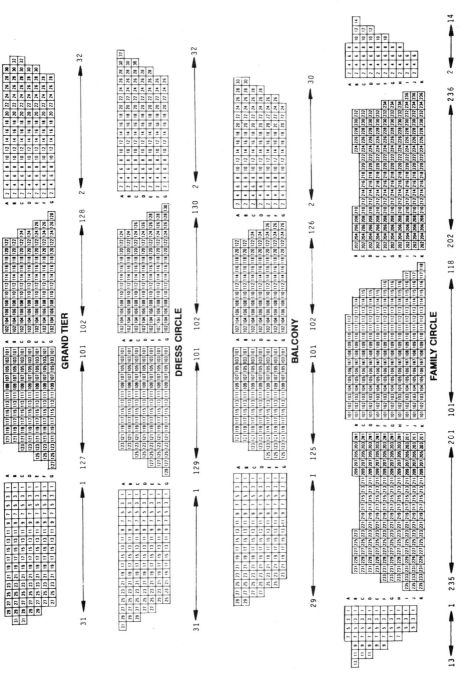

GRAND TIER

DRESS CIRCLE

BALCONY

FAMILY CIRCLE

43

*MEADOWLANDS

NJ Sports & Exposition Authority
Ticket Department, Box #512
East Rutherford, New Jersey 07073

Box Office: (201) 935-3900

Lower Tier	35,004
Mezzanine	10,101
Upper Tier	32,791
Total	77,896

Wheelchair locations
top area of Sections 117-125

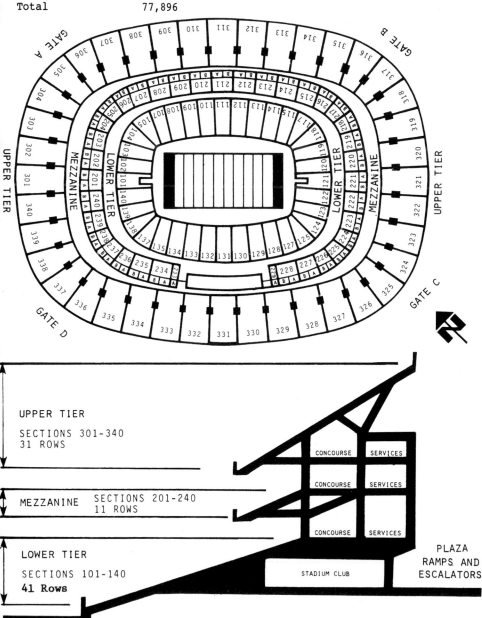

UPPER TIER

SECTIONS 301-340
31 ROWS

MEZZANINE   SECTIONS 201-240
11 ROWS

LOWER TIER

SECTIONS 101-140
41 Rows

CONCOURSE   SERVICES
CONCOURSE   SERVICES
CONCOURSE   SERVICES

STADIUM CLUB

PLAZA
RAMPS AND
ESCALATORS

* MINSKOFF THEATRE

1515 Broadway at (44th-45th Streets)
New York, New York 10036

Box Office: (212) 307-4100
Group Sales: (212) 398-8383

Wheelchair locations
Orchestra ZZ 1-11, 2-12
ZZZ 101-105, 121-125, 126, 130
Mezzanine Box Left, Box Right

Orchestra	1,101
Mezzanine	584
Total	1,685

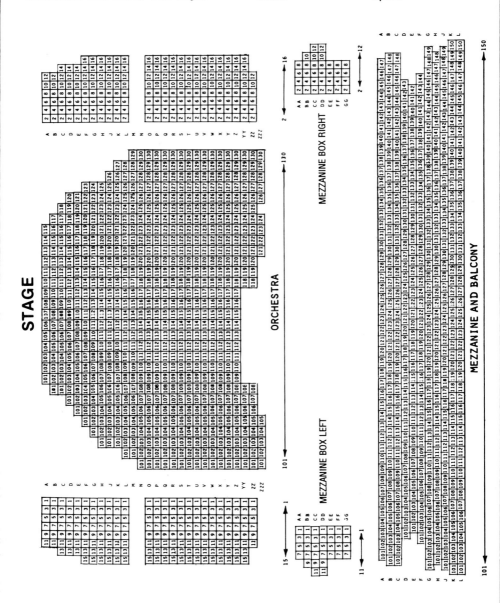

STAGE

ORCHESTRA

MEZZANINE BOX RIGHT

MEZZANINE BOX LEFT

MEZZANINE AND BALCONY

*MUSIC BOX THEATRE

239 West 45th Street
New York, New York 10036

Box Office: (212) 239-6200
Group Sales: (212) 398-8383

Orchestra   539
Boxes   16
Mezzanine   455

Total   1,010

Balcony row A overhangs Orchestra row J.

Wheelchair locations P 21, 23

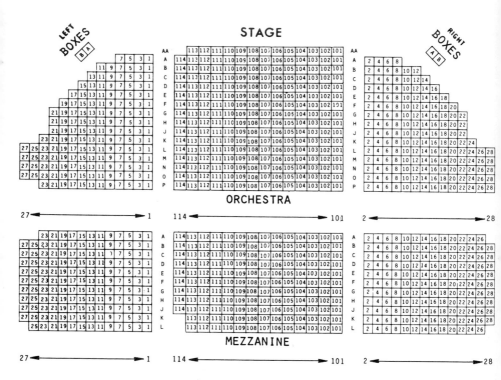

NATIONAL TENNIS CENTER

Arthur Ashe Stadium
Flushing Meadow — Corona Park
Flushing, New York 11368

Box Office: (718) 760-6200 X 5100

Total Capacity: 23,219

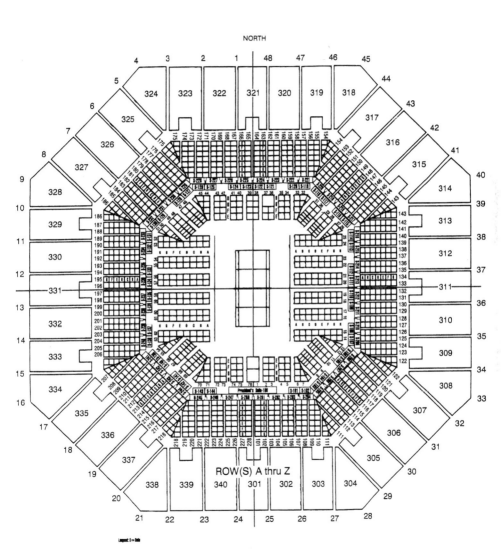

NORTH

ROW(S) A thru Z

47

*NEDERLANDER THEATRE

208 West 41st Street
New York, New York 10036

Box Office:	(212) 307-4100
Group Sales	(212) 398-8383

Orchestra	621
Mezzanine	552
Boxes	16
Total	**1,189**

Mezzanine row AA overhangs
Orchestra row G.

Wheelchair locations P 27, 28
Q 27, 28

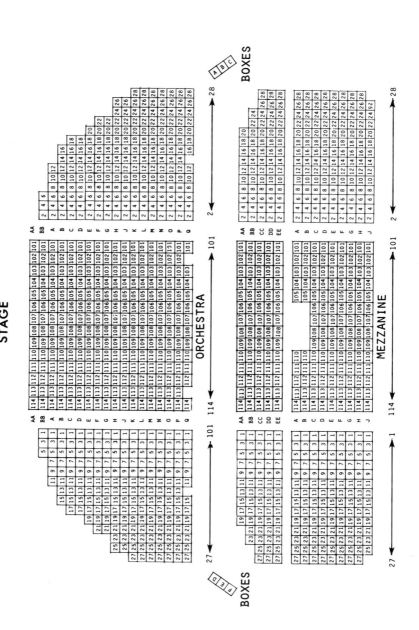

STAGE

BOXES

ORCHESTRA

MEZZANINE

BOXES

*NEW AMSTERDAM THEATRE

214 West 42nd Street
New York, New York 10036

Mezzanine overhangs Orchestra row P.
Balcony overhangs Mezzanine row DD.

Wheelchair locations
Orchestra V 101, 113,
           1, 2, 21, 22
Mezzanine KK 10-20

| Box Office: | (212) 307-4100 |
| Group Sales: | (212) 398-8383 |

Orchestra	763
Mezzanine	571
Balcony	397
Boxes	40
Total	1,771

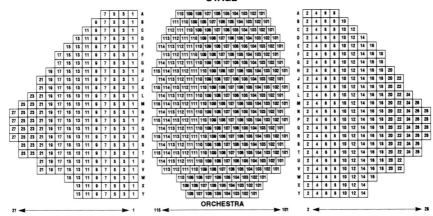

* NEW YORK STATE THEATER

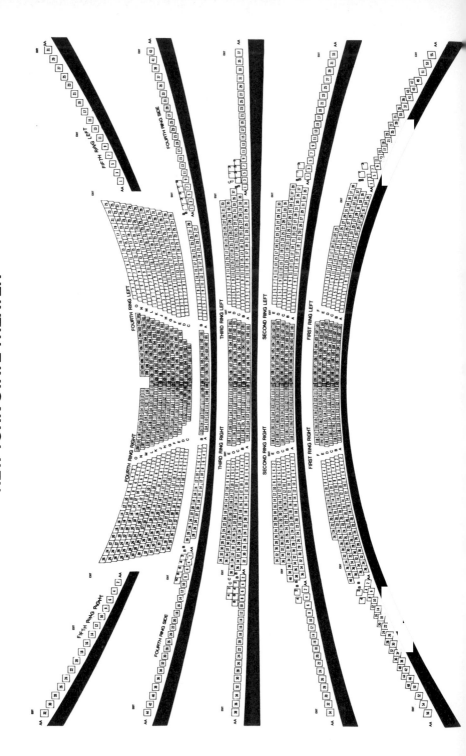

50

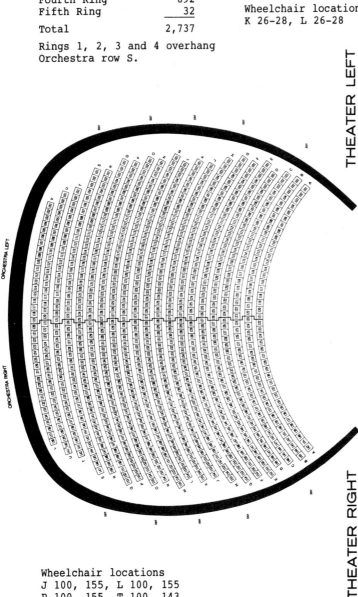

*NEW YORK STATE THEATER

Orchestra	1,048
First Ring	343
Second Ring	312
Third Ring	310
Fourth Ring	692
Fifth Ring	32
Total	2,737

Rings 1, 2, 3 and 4 overhang
Orchestra row S.

Lincoln Center
Broadway at 64th Street
New York, New York 10023

Box Office: (212) 870-5570

Wheelchair locations
K 26-28, L 26-28

THEATER LEFT

ORCHESTRA LEFT

ORCHESTRA RIGHT

THEATER RIGHT

Wheelchair locations
J 100, 155, L 100, 155
P 100, 155, T 100, 143

51

*THE NEW VICTORY THEATER

209 West 42nd Street
New York, New York 10036

Box Office:	(212) 239-6200	Mezzanine row A overhangs Orchestra row L.
Group Sales:	(212) 398-8383	Balcony row A overhangs Mezzanine row B.

Orchestra	269
Mezzanine	128
Balcony	102
Total	499

Wheelchair locations - Orchestra
and Balcony (advance notice required,
based on availability)

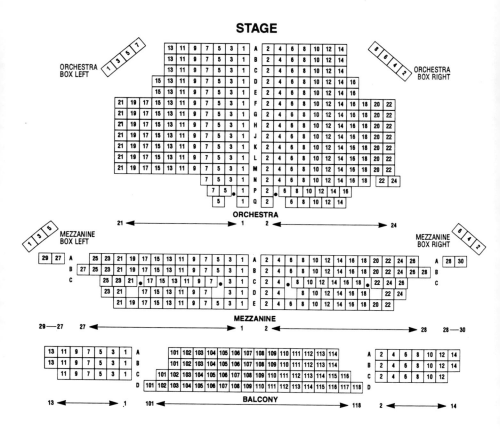

*EUGENE O'NEILL THEATRE

230 West 49th Street
New York, New York 10036

| Box Office: | (212) 239-6200 |
| Group Sales: | (212) 398-8383 |

Mezzanine row A overhangs
Orchestra row L.

Wheelchair locations
P 23-25, P 24-26,
Q 21-23, Q 22-24

Orchestra	710
Boxes	32
Front Mezzanine	160
Rear Mezzanine	204
Total	1,106

STAGE

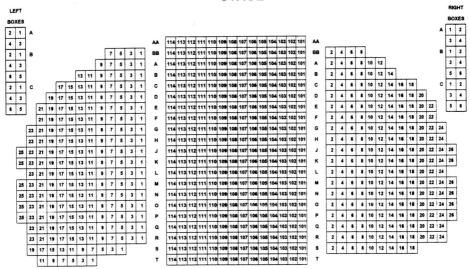

ORCHESTRA

FRONT MEZZANINE

REAR MEZZANINE

*PALACE THEATRE

1564 Broadway (at 47th Street)
New York, New York 10036

Box Office: (212) 307-4100
Group Sales: (212) 398-8383

Orchestra	830
Mezzanine	569
Balcony	301
Mezzanine Boxes	22
Balcony Boxes	18
Total	1,740

Orchestra side seats are elevated.
Mezz. row A overhangs Orch. row K.
Balc. row A overhangs Mezz. row G.

Wheelchair locations D 2, 4, 1, 3,
                      E 2, 4, 1, 3

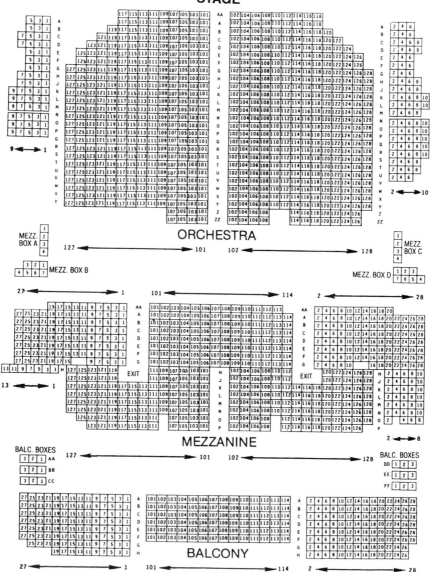

STAGE

ORCHESTRA

MEZZANINE

BALCONY

*PLYMOUTH THEATRE

236 West 45th Street
New York, New York 10036

Box Office: (212) 239-6200
Group Sales: (212) 398-8383

Orchestra	662
Boxes	24
Mezzanine	392
Total	1,078

Mezzanine row A overhangs
Orchestra row J.

Wheelchair locations
N 25-27, M 26-28

STAGE

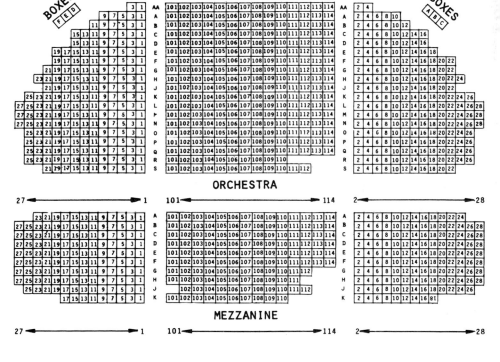

ORCHESTRA

MEZZANINE

RADIO CITY MUSIC HALL

1260 Avenue of the Americas
New York, New York 10020

Box Office: (212) 307-7171
Group Sales: (212) 398-8383

Orchestra	3,446
First Mezzanine	944
Second Mezzanine	835
Third Mezzanine	685
Total	5,910

STAGE

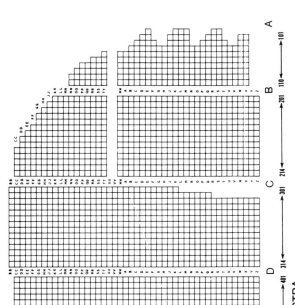

ORCHESTRA

56

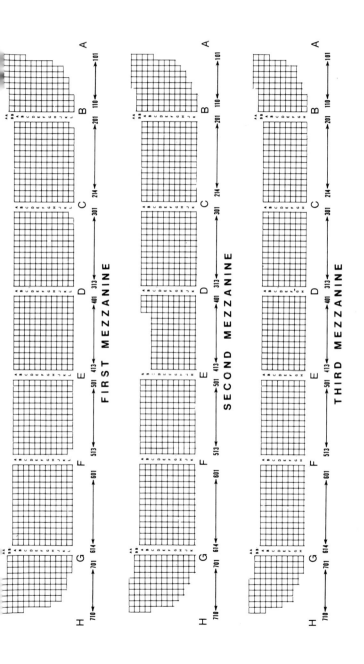

FIRST MEZZANINE

SECOND MEZZANINE

THIRD MEZZANINE

57

*RICHARD RODGERS THEATRE

226 West 46th Street
New York, New York 10036

Box Office: (212) 307-4100
Group Sales: (212) 398-8383

Orchestra	848
Boxes	32
Mezzanine	252
Rear Mezzanine	268
Total	1,400

Orchestra is elevated starting at row J.
Mezzanine row A overhangs Orchestra row L.

Wheelchair locations E 22, F 21, 22, G 21

*Orchestra AA & BB may be removed
for musicals.

STAGE

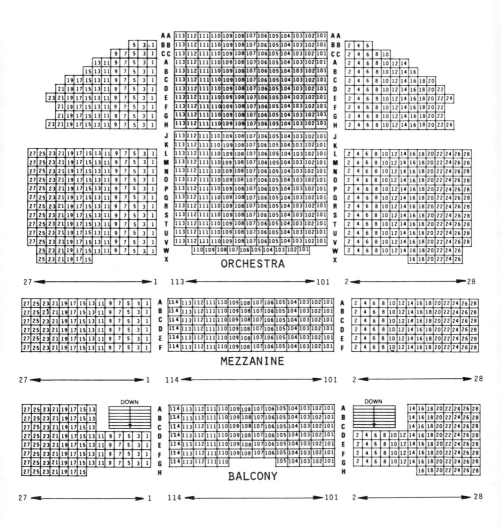

ORCHESTRA

MEZZANINE

BALCONY

*ROYALE THEATRE

242 West 45th Street
New York, New York 10036

Box Office: (212) 239-6200
Group Sales: (212) 398-8383

Wheelchair locations
K 26-28, L 26-28

Orchestra	642
Boxes	16
Mezzanine	410
Total	1,068

Mezzanine row A overhangs
Orchestra row I.

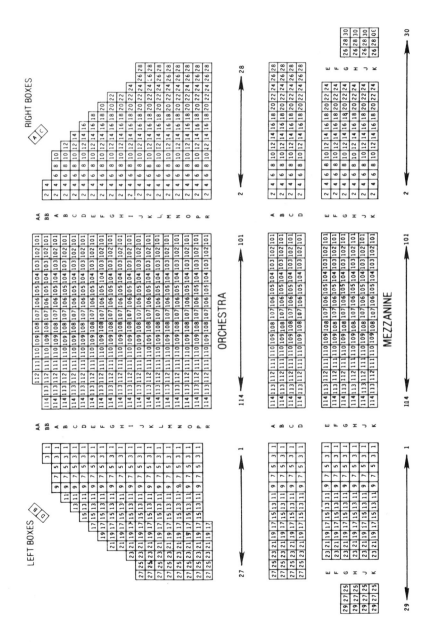

STAGE

RIGHT BOXES

LEFT BOXES

ORCHESTRA

MEZZANINE

*ST. JAMES THEATRE

246 West 44th Street
New York, New York 10036

Box Office: (212) 239-6200
Group Sales: (212) 398-8383

Orchestra	698
Boxes	20
Mezzanine	652
Balcony	320
Total	1,690

Mezzanine row A overhangs Orchestra row G.
Balcony row A overhangs Mezzanine row D.

Wheelchair locations
M 27-29, O 27-29, M 28-30, O 28-30

STAGE

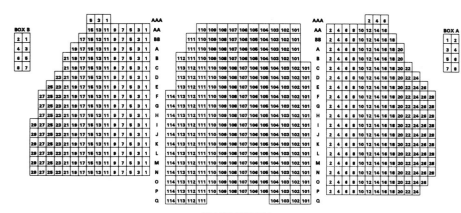

ORCHESTRA

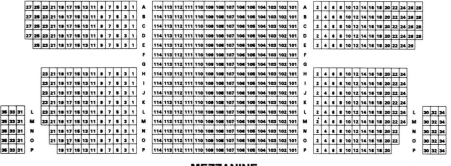

MEZZANINE

BALCONY

SHEA STADIUM

126th Street & Roosevelt Avenue
Flushing, New York 11368
Ticket Office: (718) 507-TIXX

Capacity: 55,777

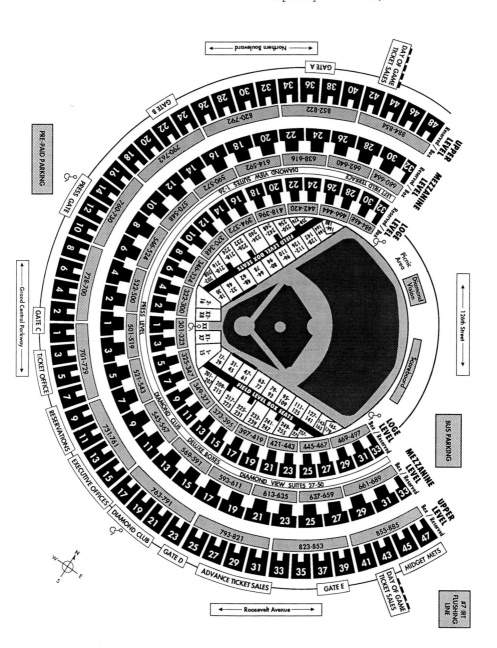

61

*SHUBERT THEATRE

225 West 44th Street
New York, New York 10036

Box Office: (212) 239-6200
Group Sales: (212) 398-8383

Orchestra	735
Boxes	16
Mezzanine	410
Balcony	352
Total	1,513

Mezzanine row A overhangs Orchestra row L.
Balcony row A overhangs Mezzanine row C.

Wheelchair locations N 23-25, O 23-25

*Orchestra capacity for musicals is 699.

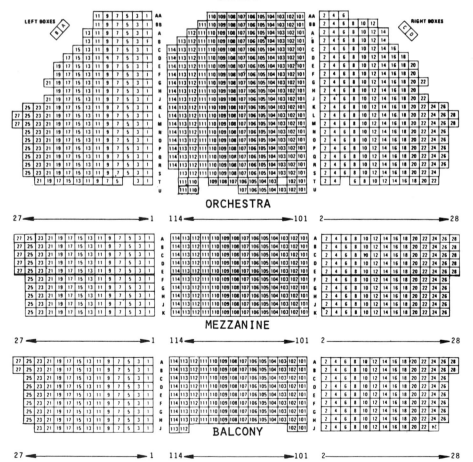

STAGE

ORCHESTRA

MEZZANINE

BALCONY

*NEIL SIMON THEATRE

250 West 52nd Street
New York, New York 10019

Box Office: (212) 307-4100
Group Sales: (212) 398-8383

Wheelchair locations
K 26-28, L 26-28

Orchestra	683
Boxes	24
Mezzanine	190
Balcony	437
Total	1,334

Mezzanine row A overhangs
Orchestra row K.

Wheelchair locations U 21, V 19

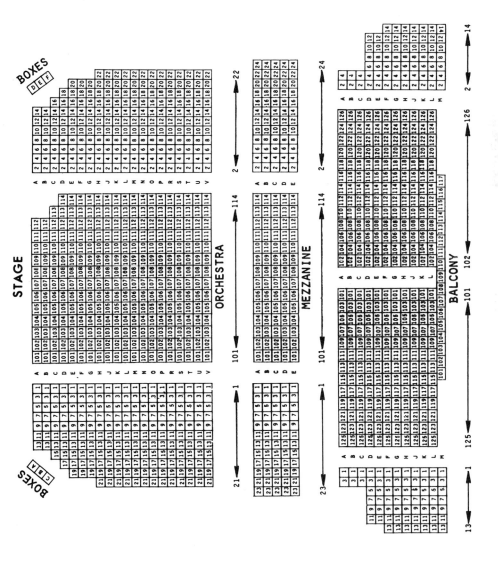

STAGE

ORCHESTRA

MEZZANINE

BALCONY

BOXES

STUDIO 54

254 West 54th Street
New York, New York 10019

Box Office: (212) 239-6200
Group Sales: (212) 398-8383

Table Seats	256
Banquettes	28
Rear Orchestra	32
Bar Seats	12
Front Mezzanine	88
Rear Mezzanine	266
Rear Mezzanine Bar Seats	36
Total	718

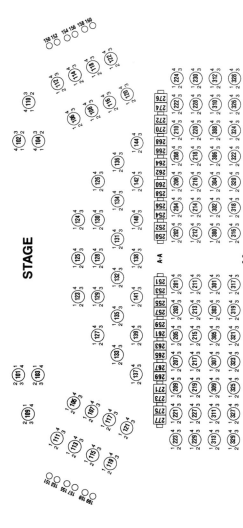

STAGE

ORCHESTRA

FRONT MEZZANINE

REAR MEZZANINE

* SYMPHONY SPACE

Orchestra 632 (+54 partial view)
Balcony 168 (+30 partial view)

Total 800 (+84 partial view)

Wheelchair locations 00 2-6, PP 4, 6,
QQ 4, 6

2537 Broadway (at 95th Street)
New York, New York 10025

Box Office: (212) 864-5400
Group Sales: (212) 398-8383

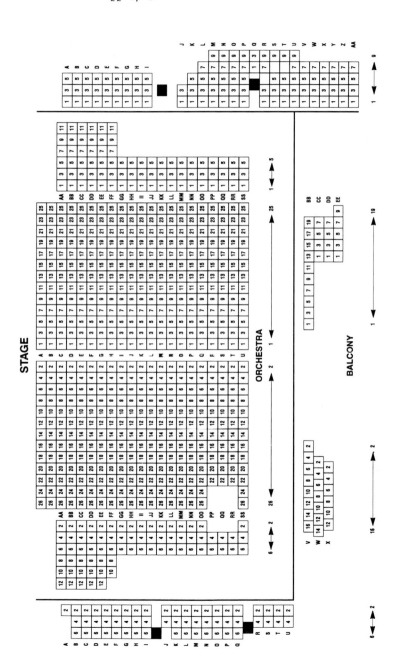

STAGE

ORCHESTRA

BALCONY

65

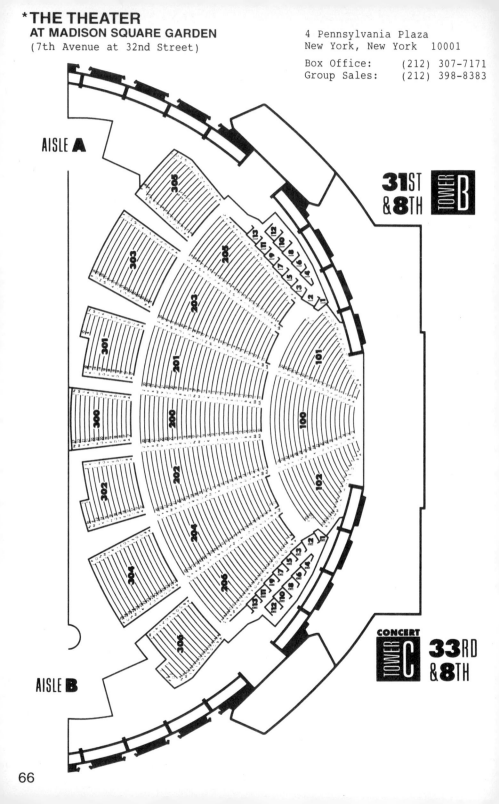

*THE THEATER
AT MADISON SQUARE GARDEN
(7th Avenue at 32nd Street)

4 Pennsylvania Plaza
New York, New York 10001

Box Office: (212) 307-7171
Group Sales: (212) 398-8383

AISLE **A**

31ST
&8TH   TOWER **B**

CONCERT
TOWER **C**   **33**RD
&8TH

AISLE **B**

TOWN HALL

Orchestra   829
Loge   78
Balcony   588
Total   1,495

123 West 43rd Street
New York, New York 10036

Box Office:(212) 840-2824

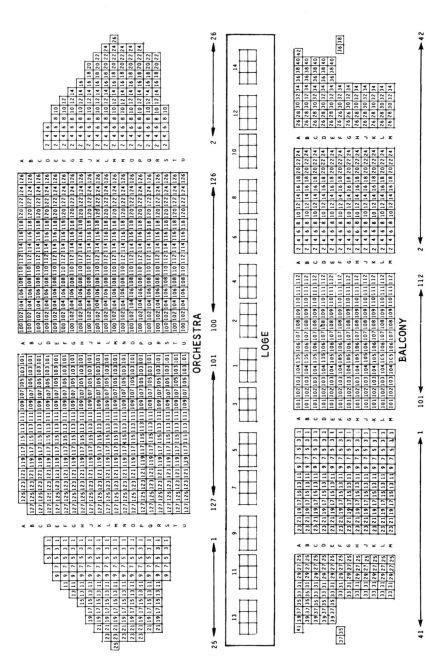

STAGE

ORCHESTRA

LOGE

BALCONY

67

*ALICE TULLY HALL

Lincoln Center
Julliard Building
Broadway at 65th Street
New York, New York 10023

Box Office: (212) 721-6500

Orchestra	936
Boxes	56
Loge	104
Total	1,096

Wheelchair locations Box C Right

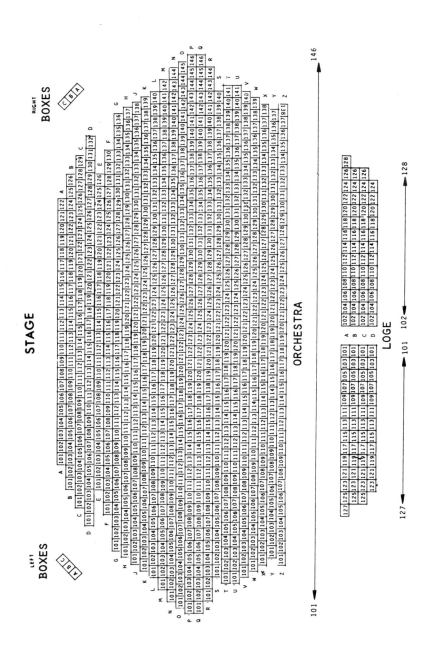

*VIRGINIA THEATRE

245 West 52nd Street
New York, New York 10019

Box Office: (212) 239-6200
Group Sales:(212) 398-8383

Mezzanine row A overhangs
Orchestra row K.

Wheelchair locations D 11-13, F 13-15
H 13-15, K 13-15

Orchestra	790
Mezzanine	485
Total	1,275

STAGE

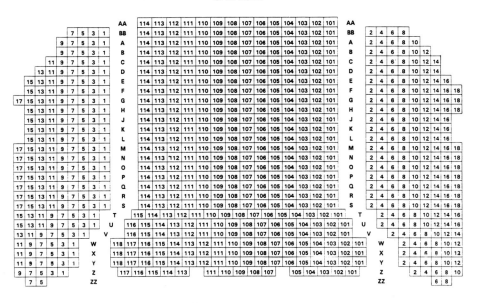

ORCHESTRA

MEZZANINE

69

* WINTER GARDEN THEATRE

1634 Broadway (at 51st Street)
New York, New York 10019

Box Office: (212) 239-6200
Group Sales: (212) 398-8383

Orchestra	933
Stage	31
Mezzanine	491
Lower Boxes	16
Upper Boxes	11
Total	1,482

Mezzanine row A overhangs
row O at center of Orchestra.

Wheelchair locations
T 28-30, U 28-30, V 28-30

STAGE

ORCHESTRA

MEZZANINE

LOWER / RIGHT BOXES / UPPER

LOWER / LEFT BOXES / UPPER

YANKEE STADIUM

River Avenue at 161st Street
Bronx, New York 10451

Box Office: (212) 203-6000

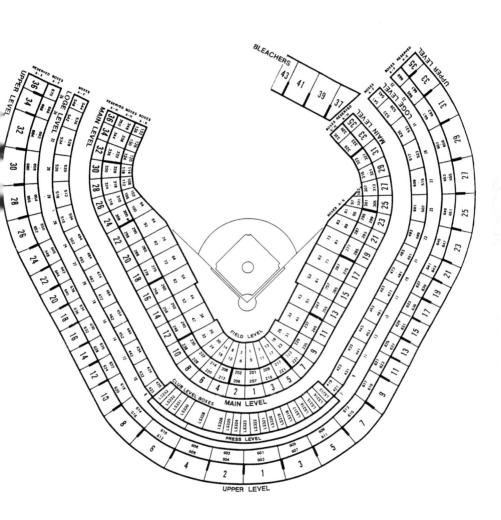

ACTOR'S PLAYHOUSE

100 Seventh Avenue South
New York, New York 10014

Box Office: (212) 239-6200
Group Sales: (212) 398-8383

Theatre Capacity: 170

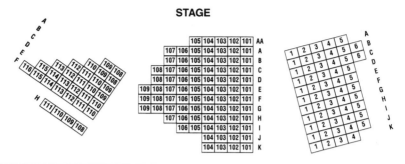

STAGE

AMERICAN JEWISH THEATRE

307 West 26th Street
New York, New York 10001

Box Office: (212) 239-6200
Group Sales (212) 398-8383

Theatre Capacity: 148

STAGE

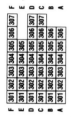

THE AMERICAN PLACE THEATRE

111 West 46th Street
New York, New York 10036

Box Office: (212) 239-6200

Theatre Capacity: 327

STAGE

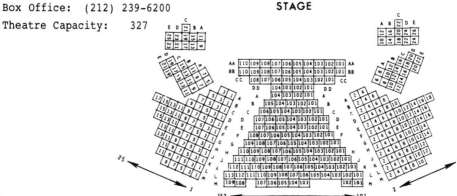

72

STAGE

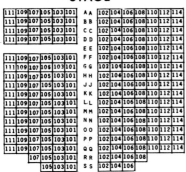

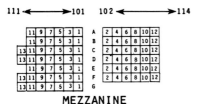

ORCHESTRA

111 ◄───► 101   102 ◄───► 114

MEZZANINE

13 ◄───► 1   2 ◄───► 12

ASTOR PLACE THEATRE

434 Lafayette Street
New York, New York 10003

Box Office: (212) 254-4370
Group Sales: (212) 398-8383

Orchestra   216
Mezzanine   82
Total   298

Mezzanine row A overhangs
Orchestra row GG.

STAGE

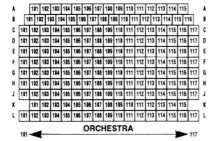

ORCHESTRA

101 ◄─────────────► 117

ATLANTIC THEATER

336 West 20th Street
New York, New York 10011

Box Office: (212) 239-6200
Group Sales: (212) 398-8383

Theatre Capacity: 182

Wheelchair location A 115

STAGE

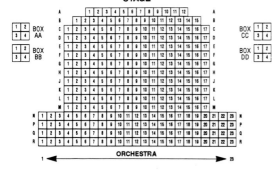

ORCHESTRA

1 ◄─────────────► 23

THE CENTURY CENTER
FOR THE PERFORMING ARTS

111 East 15th Street
New York, New York 10003

Box Office: (212)239-6200
Group Sales: (212)398-8383

Theatre Capacity 299

Wheelchair location
first 3 rows
(6 stations available)

CHERRY LANE THEATRE

38 Commerce Street
New York, New York 10014

Box Office: (212) 239-6200
Group Sales: (212) 398-8383

Theatre Capacity: 180

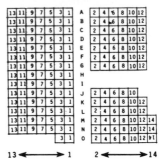

*DOUGLAS FAIRBANKS THEATRE

432 West 42nd Street
New York, New York 10036

Box Office: (212) 239-6200
Group Sales: (212) 398-8383

Theatre Capacity: 199

Wheelchair locations D 1, 2

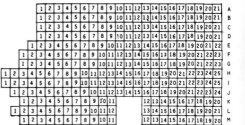

GRAMERCY THEATER

127 East 23rd Street
New York, New York 10010

Box Office: (212) 307-4100
Group Sales: (212) 398-8383

Theatre Capacity: 499

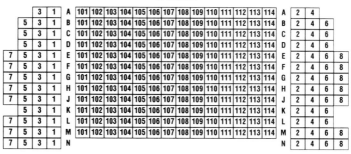

*JOHN HOUSEMAN THEATRE

STAGE

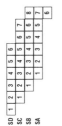

450 West 42nd Street
New York, New York 10036

Box Office: (212) 239-6200
Group Sales: (212) 398-8383

Theatre Capacity: 286

Wheelchair locations A 1, 2

IRISH REPERTORY THEATRE

132 West 22nd Street
New York, New York 10011

Box Office: (212) 727-2737
Group Sales: (212) 398-8383

Theatre Capacity: 137

STAGE

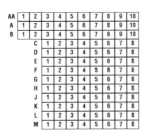

*KAUFMAN THEATRE

STAGE

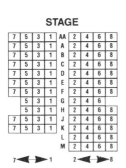

534 West 42nd Street
New York, New York 10036

Box Office: (212) 239-6200
Group Sales: (212) 398-8383

Theatre Capacity: 93

Wheelchair location K 1-7

LAMB'S THEATRE (MAINSTAGE)

130 West 44th Street
New York, New York 10036

Box Office: (212) 997-1780
Group Sales: (212) 398-8383

Orchestra	244
Boxes	24
Mezzanine	81
Total	349

Mezzanine row AA overhangs
Orchestra row E.

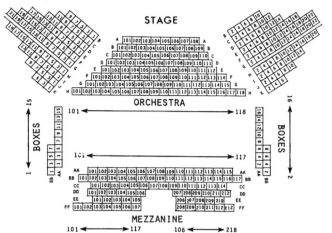

*LUCILLE LORTEL THEATRE

121 Christopher Street
New York, New York 10014

Box Office: (212) 239-6200
Group Sales: (212) 398-8383

Orchestra	235
Mezzanine	64
Total	299

Mezzanine row A overhangs
Orchestra row F.

Wheelchair locations B 6, 8

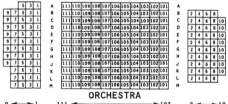

*MANHATTAN THEATRE CLUB AT CITY CENTER THEATRE

131 West 55th Street
New York, New York 10019

Box Office: (212) 239-6200
Group Sales: (212) 398-8383

Theatre Capacity: 299

Wheelchair locations
adjoining A 5, 6

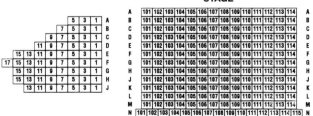

*MINETTA LANE THEATRE

Orchestra	285
Mezzanine	122
Total	407

Mezzanine row A overhangs
Orchestra row J.

Wheelchair locations 0 1, 2, P 1, 2

18 Minetta Lane
New York, New York 10012

Box Office: (212) 420-8000
Group Sales: (212) 398-8383

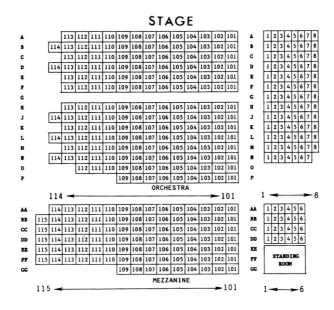

*THE MITZI E. NEWHOUSE THEATER

Theatre Capacity: 299
Wheelchair location H 31

Lincoln Center
150 West 65th Street
New York, New York 10023

Box Office: (212) 239-6200
Group Sales: (212) 398-8383

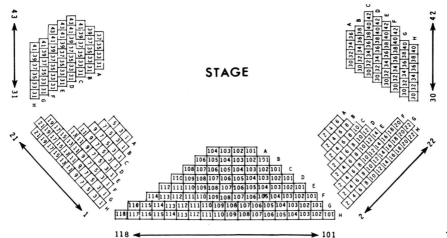

NEW YORK SHAKESPEARE FESTIVAL THEATERS

The Joseph Papp Public Theater
425 Lafayette Street — New York, New York 10003

Box Office: (212) 239-6200
Group Sales Box Office: (212) 398-8383

*ANSPACHER THEATER

Theatre Capacity: 277

Wheelchair locations A 1, 2 House Left

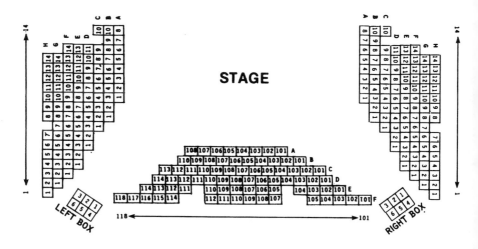

*LU ESTHER HALL

Theatre Capacity: 159

Wheelchair locations A 310, 302

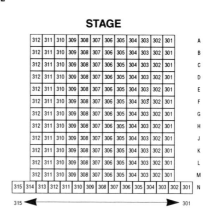

NEW YORK SHAKESPEARE FESTIVAL THEATERS

The Joseph Papp Public Theater
425 Lafayette Street — New York, New York 10003

Box Office: (212) 239-6200
Group Sales Box Office: (212) 398-8383

*MARTINSON HALL

Theatre Capacity: 193

Wheelchair locations
AA 1, 2

STAGE

13	12	11	10	9	8	7	6	5	4	3	2	1	AA
13	12	11	10	9	8	7	6	5	4	3	2	1	BB
13	12	11	10	9	8	7	6	5	4	3	2	1	CC
13	12	11	10	9	8	7	6	5	4	3	2	1	DD
13	12	11	10	9	8	7	6	5	4	3	2	1	EE
13	12	11	10	9	8	7	6	5	4	3	2	1	FF
13	12	11	10	9	8	7	6	5	4	3	2	1	GG
13	12	11	10	9	8	7	6	5	4	3	2	1	HH
13	12	11	10	9	8	7	6	5	4	3	2	1	JJ
13	12	11	10	9	8	7	6	5	4	3	2	1	KK
13	12	11	10	9	8	7	6	5	4	3	2	1	LL
13	12	11	10	9	8	7	6	5	4	3	2	1	MM
13	12	11	10	9	8	7	6	5	4	3	2	1	NN
13	12	11	10	9		7	6	5	4	3	2	1	OO
	12	11	10	9		7	6	5	4	3	2		PP

13 ← → 1

*NEWMAN THEATER

Theatre Capacity: 299

Wheelchair locations
A 1, 2, 3

STAGE

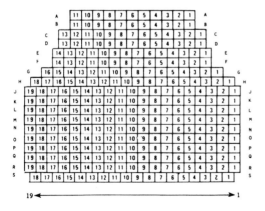

19 ← → 1

*SUSAN STEIN SHIVA THEATER

Theatre Capacity: 109

Wheelchair locations A 101, 102

STAGE

116	115	114	113	112	111	110	109		108	107	106	105	104	103	102	101	A
116	115	114	113	112	111	110	109		108	107	106	105	104	103	102	101	B
116	115	114	113	112	111	110	109		108	107	106	105	104	103	102	101	C
116	115	114	113	112	111	110	109		108	107	106	105	104	103	102	101	D
116	115	114	113	112	111	110	109		108	107	106	105	104	103	102	101	E
108	107	106	105						104	103	102	101					F
110	109	108	107	106					105	104	105	102	101				G
111	110	109	108	107					106	105	104	103	102	101			H

116 ← → 101

79

ORPHEUM THEATRE

126 Second Avenue
New York, New York 10003

Box Office: (212) 447-2477
Group Sales: (212) 398-8383

Orchestra   273
Mezzanine   74

Total   347

Balcony row AA overhangs
Orchestra row J

Wheelchair locations J 9, 11

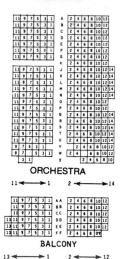

STAGE

ORCHESTRA

11 ←——→ 1   2 ←——→ 14

BALCONY

13 ←——→ 1   2 ←——→ 12

PLAYERS THEATRE

115 MacDougal Street
New York, New York 10012

Box Office: (212) 254-5076
Group Sales: (212) 398-8383

Theatre Capacity: 248

Wheelchair locations
Behind row T, even side

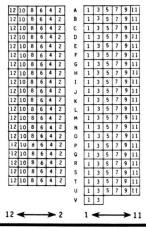

STAGE

12 ←——→ 2   1 ←——→ 11

PLAYHOUSE 91

316 East 91st Street
New York, New York 10128

Box Office: (212) 831-2000
Group Sales: (212) 398-8383

Theatre Capacity: 299

STAGE

14 ←——→ 2   101 ←——————→ 114   1 ←—→ 5

80

STAGE

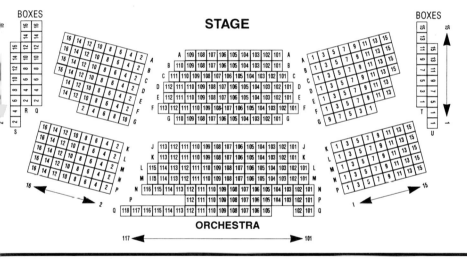

Orchestra	359
Boxes	40
Total	399

Wheelchair location Q 101

PROMENADE THEATRE

2162 Broadway (at 76th Street)
New York, New York 10024

Box Office: (212) 239-6200
Group Sales: (212) 398-8383

BOXES   **STAGE**   **BOXES**

ORCHESTRA

Orchestra	284
Boxes	12
Total	296

Wheelchair locations
A 106-111, 3-6, O 108-113

SECOND STAGE THEATRE

307 West 43rd Street
New York, New York 10036

Box Office: (212) 246-4422
Group Sales: (212) 398-8383

STAGE

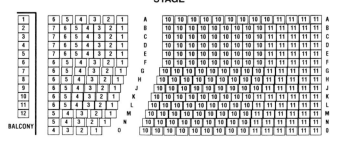

81

*SIGNATURE THEATRE

555 West 42nd Street
(10th & 11th Aves.)
New York, New York 10036

Box Office: (212) 244-PLAY
Group Sales: (212) 398-8383

Theatre Capacity: 160

STAGE

SOHO PLAYHOUSE

15 Vandam Street
New York, New York 10013

Box Office: (212) 239-6200
Group Sales: (212) 398-8383

Theatre Capacity: 214

STAGE

SULLIVAN STREET PLAYHOUSE

181 Sullivan Street
New York, New York 10012

Box Office: (212) 674-3838
Group Sales: (212) 398-8383

Theatre Capacity: 153

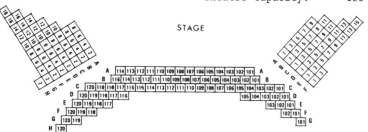

STAGE

*THEATER FOUR

424 West 55th Street
New York, New York 10019

Box Office: (212) 239-6200
Group Sales: (212) 398-8383

Orchestra   212
Mezzanine   42

Total   254

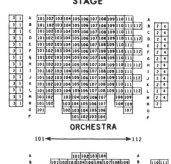

STAGE

ORCHESTRA

101 ◄──────► 112

MEZZANINE

101 ◄──────► 111

UNION SQUARE THEATRE

Orchestra	339
Mezzanine	160
Total	499

100 East 17th Street
New York, New York 10003

Box Office: (212) 505-0700
Group Sales: (212) 398-8383

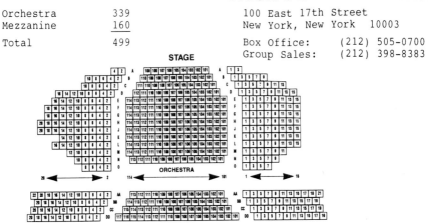

VARIETY ARTS THEATRE

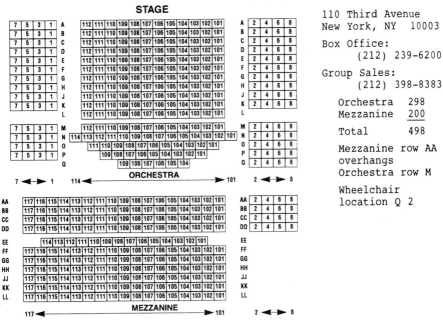

110 Third Avenue
New York, NY 10003

Box Office:
    (212) 239-6200

Group Sales:
    (212) 398-8383

Orchestra	298
Mezzanine	200
Total	498

Mezzanine row AA
overhangs
Orchestra row M

Wheelchair
location Q 2

WPA THEATRE AT THE CHELSEA PLAYHOUSE

519 West 23rd Street
New York, New York 10011

Box Office: (212) 239-6200

Theatre Capacity: 128

83

WESTSIDE THEATRE (UPSTAIRS)

407 West 43rd Street
New York, New York 10036

Box Office: (212) 239-6200
Group Sales (212) 398-8383

Theatre Capacity: 299

STAGE

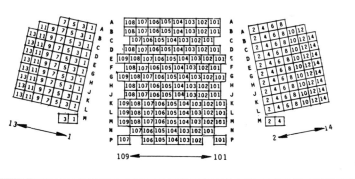

7 ←→ 1   112 ←——————————→ 101   2 ←→ 8

WESTSIDE THEATRE (DOWNSTAIRS)

407 West 43rd Street
New York, New York 10036

Box Office: (212) 239-6200
Group Sales: (212) 398-8383

Theatre Capacity: 250

STAGE

13 ←——→ 1   109 ←——— 101   2 ←——→ 14

YORK THEATRE AT ST. PETER'S CHURCH

(Citicorp Center at 54th Street)
619 Lexington Avenue
New York, New York 10022-4610

Box Office: (212) 935-5820
Group Sales: (212) 398-8383

Theatre Capacity: 147

Wheelchair locations A 15, 16

STAGE

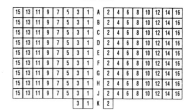